My Stuffed Animals

By Ann Staman

Illustrated by Tatjana Mai-Wyss

Here is my bear.

I like my bear.

Here is my monkey.

I like my monkey.

Here is my lion.

I like my lion.

7

Here is Tiger.

I like Tiger.

Here is my hippo.

I like my hippo.

Here is my snake.

13

Here is my elephant.

15

I like my zoo.